NO NONSENSE PARENTING GUIDE

FATHERING

OTHER NO NONSENSE PARENTING GUIDES

Pregnancy, Birth and Bonding
Your Growing Baby
Feeding Your Baby
Play and Learn
The Working Mother
Raising A Happy Baby
Your Baby's Health and Safety

OTHER NO NONSENSE GUIDES

Real Estate Guides
Financial Guides
Legal Guides
Career Guides
Success Guides
Health Guides
Cooking Guides
Wine Guides

NO NONSENSE PARENTING GUIDE™

Fathering

PLAYING YOUR PART IN PREGNANCY, BIRTH AND BEYOND

Robert Ostermann, Christopher Spurrell, and Carolyn T. Chubet

LONGMEADOW PRESS

FATHERING

Copyright © 1988 by Carolyn T. Chubet

No Nonsense Parenting Guide is a trademark controlled by Longmeadow Press.

Published by Longmeadow Press, 201 High Ridge Road, Stamford, Connecticut 06904. No part of this book may be reproduced or used in any form or by any means, electronic or mechanical, including photocopying, recording, or by an information storage and retrieval system, without permission in writing from the publisher.

ISBN 0-681-40451-5

Printed in the United States of America

0 9 8 7 6 5 4 3 2 1

PREPARED FOR LONGMEADOW PRESS BY
IRENA CHALMERS BOOKS, INC.

MANAGING EDITOR: Jean Atcheson
COVER DESIGN: Karen Skelton
ART DIRECTION & DESIGN: Helene Berinsky
PICTURE RESEARCHER: Lisa Sorensen
TYPESETTING: ComCom, Allentown, Pennsylvania
PRODUCTION SERVICES: William S. Konecky Associates, New York

Cover photograph © 1988 Penny Gentieu

Contents

For Deirdre, Liam, Darina, Denise and
Shaw; for Cailyn and Katie; for John,
Charlie—and Tom

ACKNOWLEDGMENTS

Our thanks to Malcolm M. Brown, M.D., of the Sharon, Connecticut,
Pediatric Association, and to Judy Kay Morris, R.N., Certified Nurse-
Midwife with the Sharon, Connecticut, Ob-Gyn Associates, for their
insightful comments on the subject of fathering and babies.

Introduction

Welcome to fatherhood! You have made the move to Life's Major League. Suddenly you are a man with a purpose, and life has new meaning. You feel almost superhuman, ready to leap tall buildings, etc. Unfortunately, that isn't the whole story. This monumental change brings more than joy and strength into your life. It also entails some heavy-duty responsibility and conjures up a host of worries.

In the beginning, all this may overwhelm you. But you won't be so intimidated if you approach fathering one step at a time. Becoming a father is a rite of passage that evolves over months and months. As you travel through each stage of the ritual—pregnancy, birth and nurturing your baby—a new dimension will be added to your personality. The man you become will be able to handle any situation that fatherhood demands. As you take each hurdle cleanly, you will build new confidence.

Fathering is what you make it. Biologically, you have already done the only job you absolutely *have* to do! You could walk away and leave your wife with the rest of the process. Some men do. But obviously you aren't going to do that, or you wouldn't be reading this book. You are intrigued with fathering and want to discover its possibilities. By doing so, you are joining a vanguard of men who commit themselves profoundly to the babies they have made.

Fathers in this country have had a tough time getting off the periphery of parenting and into the mainstream. Their greatest obstacles have been cultural. Social values and attitudes, behavioral patterns and self-image have all reinforced the traditional role of fathers solely in economic terms. If you were a generous and dependable provider, you could feel that you were a good father. You had measured up.

Beyond that, what was there? Fathers were just about invisible in the self-help articles and books, which focused on the mother-to-be. If you took these works seriously, men had no emotional connection with their partners that pregnancy might disrupt, and were expected to be immune to the turbulence following childbirth and the intrusion of a totally dependent human being into what had been an exclusive twosome. Fathers were little more than spectators at the drama of pregnancy, birth and beyond.

Also ignored was the possibility that being a father might enrich you, stretch your emotional range, breach the existing frontiers of your relationship with your wife and give you an exciting role in creating a new community: the family. Fortunately, that tradition is rapidly being replaced by a more generous one that puts fathers where they belong, at the very center of the parenting experience.

As you join other men who have discovered the joy and challenge of fathering, you will find that some of your responses to the experience and solutions to its problems may be different from those of your friends. Just as no two people are alike, no two families are alike. Don't judge yourself by the casual responses and opinions of others. They aren't *you* and can't be in a position to know your situation.

In pregnancy and parenting there are few universal truths to follow. More often than not, you will find yourself swinging from branch to branch of "if, then" statements, moving from one decision point to the next. Good medical advice, careful thought and planning, and a healthy dose of common sense will get you and your new family safely from point A to point B. There are no pat answers. The more flexible you can be, the easier and more rewarding the whole experience will be—for you, your wife and your baby.

Fathering is intended to help you on your way. We'll discuss many of the principal joys and anxieties you will find yourself facing and suggest ways to handle some of the difficulties that lie ahead. We'll take the challenge of pregnancy, childbirth and parenting and break it down into manageable pieces. And we'll encourage you to share each step with your wife. If you and she work together, the intimate circle of your marriage will gradually expand. And when the time comes, you will both be ready to receive the baby with joy and gladness.

As you and your partner go through pregnancy together and into the unfolding experience of a family, it might also help to keep this maxim before you:

Don't be the kind of father others may think you ought to be. Be the kind of father you will be proud to be.

Because approximately equal numbers of boy and girl babies are born—fortunately for the human race—we refer to your baby as "he" or "she" in alternate chapters of this book.

CHAPTER 1

Changes: Understanding Pregnancy

The moment your mate became pregnant your whole world changed, and with the news came a new set of rules and roles. The part your wife plays is clearly defined: She is physically pregnant. She has the immediate task of coping with the changes wrought by hormones in her body. From Day One they are on the job, supervising the baby's development, as well as causing many of pregnancy's discomforts. Most important of all, she must nurture this tiny life you have made with your sperm and her egg, from a microdot of potential to full-term reality.

While your partner has the physical role in the pregnancy, you must both adjust to the change which is scrambling up your lives. *You,* the father-to-be, are psychologically pregnant. In these unsettled months, you are worried. What is happening to our relationship? What will happen to our relationship when the baby comes? Can we afford it? Should we have waited?

As time goes by, you will get used to the idea of having a baby. Your worries will fade, but don't expect them to disappear altogether. Doubts will linger until after the baby is born. Try to put them away. Remember that babies are born—and raised—successfully all the time. Your baby's future is not dependent on how much you worry! It is much better to spend your emotional energy on the step-by-step approach to fathering included in these pages.

The baby growing in your wife's womb signals that some changes lie ahead. Indeed, it is a clear new beginning. The months of pregnancy are a grace period, allowing new parents to settle in gradually. If you use the time wisely, you will be ready when the baby is. (If you are reading this book for the first time at the end of your partner's pregnancy, it is not too late to catch up.)

As you grow into parenthood, you naturally reorganize your priorities and your philosophy. While you are redefining the meaning of life, keep one priority from the old days on top: your relationship. It is vital that you keep the lines

---

ESTIMATING YOUR BABY'S DUE DATE

Your baby will be born approximately 40 weeks after conception. To calculate the estimated due date (EDD), you and your wife will count back three months from the first day of her last period and add seven days. Remember that this is only an approximation. There is a two-week window before and after that particular day.

---

of communication open as you set your course as new parents. You will need huge reserves of patience and understanding as emotions fluctuate during pregnancy. Be prepared to be sometimes puzzled, hurt or angry.

You know how you feel. As much as you might try to imagine on your own what pregnancy is like, you won't be able to. That's why it is important to find out how *she* feels. Explore her experience now as her pregnancy advances, and later when she is home with the baby. Talk with her. Listen to her. Tell her how you feel. Chances are, you'll be closer to her than *ever*.

The Three Trimesters of Pregnancy

Your baby's rapid development is a major biological feat accomplished in a very short time. So much happens so fast that it almost seems like watching a time-lapse film of a flower bud coming into bloom. And, of course, it is all the more wonderful because it is your very own baby.

For both baby and mother the nine months of pregnancy fall naturally into three segments, or trimesters. Even though no two babies or pregnancies are alike, each three-month section has a flavor and characteristics all its own:

MONTHS 1 TO 3

Your baby: The first three months are critical for your baby. The baby's entire skeletal framework is formed with hands and feet, fingers and toes. Her face appears. Her heart starts beating and tiny muscles are flexing their might.

By the end of three months she's a mighty two inches long (remember, she started out about the size of the period at the end of this sentence). In this trimester, if something isn't right with the fetus, it may well spontaneously abort (the medical term for miscarriage). We'll discuss that in a later section.

Your wife: She is probably tired much of the time and may not have much energy. She may feel very sick at the sight of food. She may go to bed for the night ten minutes after she gets home from work. She will continue to feel this way until the placenta, which oversees the baby's development and is being formed during these first three months, can take over the work of the pregnancy. She's worried about miscarriage and won't feel relieved until this trimester is over.

MONTHS 4 TO 6

Your baby: Your baby develops her bone structure as preliminary cartilage turns into bone. Her brain develops and she begins to make her presence known—doing butterfly kicks and double back flips. She may even suck her thumb. By the end of six months she has grown two and a half times her length at three months. She is about 12 inches long and weighs more than a pound.

Your wife: This is the golden age. Her complexion glows. She is truly radiant. She regains a good deal of strength, as well as her appetite. Your baby is nestled in and the placenta takes charge.

MONTHS 7 TO 9

Your baby: She gets some final touches, including important antibodies to help fight disease, and a protective covering for her skin. She puts on a final growth spurt, gaining a half pound to a full pound each week and

HOW IT FEELS TO BE PREGNANT

Every pregnancy is different, but there are some common denominators to be aware of. The following is a list of physical changes her body is going through and some ways you can help her cope:

What Happens	Why	What You Can Do
Radical mood swings and weepy spells	Dramatic increase in hormonal activity	Give her your love and understanding.
Sore breasts	Hormonal activity preparing them for nursing	Avoid caressing or fondling them during lovemaking.
Stretched abdomen with organs becoming increasingly crowded	The baby's growth	Support her need for many small meals; help her avoid spicy foods and add fiber for good digestion.
Inability to sleep	Bad dreams, baby kicking, the frequent need to urinate	Massage her, encourage other relaxation techniques; give her the comfort of snuggling.
Heaviness and awkwardness in the third trimester	Increased size of the pregnancy; loosening of pelvic joints in preparation for childbirth	Don't insist that she dance with you or expect her to move around as she used to.

growing a total of about eight more inches. As your baby grows, she has much less room to romp and your wife's abdomen will roll when she does. You may even see a lump pop up temporarily when she kicks.

If she is born in the middle of this trimester she'll have about a 90 percent chance of survival. A full-term baby averages about 20 inches in length and about 7.7 or 7.8 pounds.

Your wife: She is growing so heavy that moving around may be an effort for her. She begins to wish that the baby were already born. You both find it hard to wait for the birth.

Those Morning Blues, Grays and Blahs

About half of all women experience the nausea of morning sickness in the first three months. For these women the smell or sight of food is unpleasant indeed. Despite the

HOW MUCH A SAMPLE PREGNANCY WEIGHS	
Baby	7.5 lbs.
Placenta	2 lbs.
Amniotic fluid	2 lbs.
Maternal blood volume	4 lbs.
Uterus, breast tissue	4 lbs.
Extracellular fluid	4 lbs.
Maternal fat stores	2 lbs.
Total	25.5 lbs.

"I DON'T KNOW HOW TO COOK" MEALS

Don't think of asking her to cook. Do as much of the meal preparation as you can, and try to make meals as tempting for her as you can manage.

If you can't cook, this is the time to learn. To stem starvation while you learn, here's a short list of balanced meals that you can make. Don't worry if dinner looks like breakfast sometimes; breakfast foods are often comfort foods, just right for a fragile stomach. Use the list below for inspiration. A little of this, a little of that, and voilà, you've got a meal fit for a baby.

- Plain or vanilla yogurt in a bowl, topped with a crunchy bran cereal and raisins or other fruit.
- Peanut butter spread on one or two slices of whole wheat toast, topped with sliced bananas.
- Chef's salad: sliced deli turkey, ham and a mild cheese on a bed of shredded lettuce with a creamy bottled dressing (tomatoes and cucumbers may be added if desired). Tuna from a can or a hard-cooked egg may be substituted for the meats.
- Blender magic. Start with a pint of skimmed milk, add ¼ cup wheat germ or bran, 1-2 tablespoons honey, bananas or other favorite fruit. Whirl until thoroughly blended.

Remember: Bland foods are more appealing to a delicate stomach than rich, spicy or fried foods.

name, morning sickness doesn't happen only in the morning. Some women are hit later in the day, or are offended by certain foods and odors at any time. Morning sickness varies in intensity: Some women have trouble keeping anything down, while others need simply to be very particular about what they eat.

Appetite Running Wild

Stories are legion about the crazy food longings of pregnant women: pickles and ice cream at midnight, applesauce laced with ketchup, salads with french fries. Such cravings probably belong more to folklore than to facts. Reality is much less exotic. Pregnant women usually tilt toward the starchy end of the table on the one hand and citrus fruits on the other.

Bizarre food can be limited; more important is to keep a runaway appetite in check and to ensure a nutritious diet. She shouldn't eat double the amount of food because she is eating for two. She really needs only a few hundred extra calories (the amount she needs depends on her metabolism and the amount of exercise she gets).

Many doctors recommend that women should gain only about 25 pounds steadily and gradually throughout the pregnancy. For example, if your wife gained half a pound a week during the first 20 weeks and a pound a week during the last 20 weeks, she would gain 30 pounds. The theory is that excess weight tends to hang on stubbornly after pregnancy is over, and might delay your wife's return to her old self as soon as possible. However, some women gain much more weight than is generally recommended *and* are able to lose it all afterwards.

You can play a significant role here by not indulging your taste for hamburgers, pastries and the empty calories of alcohol. Perhaps the fact that she probably should abstain from alcohol completely will inspire you to abstain as well. It is hard for her to be a saint when the devil is at her elbow.

TIP: *If she has trouble with temptation, you need to set an extra-good example at home.* But *the goodies you eat at*

DAILY MENU: THE FOUR BASIC FOOD GROUPS

Your wife's medical team will give her a dietary menu to follow during pregnancy and she should follow it as closely as possible. The diet plan she receives will probably include:

TYPE	MAIN BENEFITS
1. Milk and milk products, including cheese, yogurt and cottage cheese, the lower in fat the better	Calcium to build your new baby's bones and other vital functions
2. Meats, chicken and fish, concentrating on the lower fat cuts, with any skin removed	Protein to build your baby's tissues
3. Vegetables and fruits, including the dark green and yellow vegetables, and citrus fruits as well as other kinds	Vitamins A, B and C for general health of mother and baby
4. Grains, breads and cereals, preferably the high-bran, whole wheat variety	B vitamins (see above) and fiber for good digestion

a business lunch or the mound of french fries that disappears every lunch hour at your desk are your business alone.

Sometimes the ravenous pregnant appetite can be traced to sources other than hunger. Problems of self-image and other insecurities can surface as "I want to eat . . . ." What she may be saying is: "I'm worried. I'm not attractive. I'm

HEALTHY GUIDELINES FOR HER PREGNANCY

What	Why
No cigarettes (it would be best not to smoke around her either)	Dangers of miscarriage and premature delivery, low birthweight
Little or no alcohol	The dangers of moderate consumption to the fetus are not as yet well understood. Brain damage and other abnormalities are often the result of heavy drinking during pregnancy.
No recreational drugs, like marijuana and cocaine	Little is known about the effects on pregnancy and it is common sense to avoid taking risks with a baby's fragile life.
No prescription or *non*prescription drugs without consulting her doctor	Little is known about the effects of many medicines on pregnancy. Common medicines like aspirin and antihistamines should probably be avoided. Some antibiotics, tranquilizers and hormones are known to cause malformations.
Caffeine in moderation	Caffeine was long suspected to be dangerous in pregnancy, but recent findings discount the risk. Keep in mind, however, that caffeine (a) enters the fetal bloodstream and (b) may interfere with your wife's sleep.

Pregnancy is a time for togetherness and quiet pleasures—such as reading the Sunday paper

not loved." In fact, she is confronted with a direct choice between you and the refrigerator. Make it your business that she picks you.

Social Butterflies

Your social life may be much quieter now and you may have to be more selective about your social engagements. Say goodbye to spontaneity and hello to thoughtful planning. The invitations you accept or proffer must be tailored

PHYSICAL CHANGES, BODILY DISCOMFORTS

Your wife may complain of physical ailments during pregnancy. Sometimes all you can do is to listen with a sympathetic ear. Sometimes you can offer real relief.

Complaint	Possible Causes	Possible Remedies
Backache	Uterus exerting pressure on lower back; ligaments or joints loosening	Remind her to stand straight; offer her massage, a heating pad; remind her to sleep on her side, knees up
Constipation	Intestines blocked by uterus; bowel-needed water absorbed elsewhere; hormonal activity blocking digestion	See that she drinks extra water and eats bran and fiber, prunes; take a walk with her
Tiredness	Sedative power of progesterone; feature of early pregnancy before placenta takes over; natural feature of late pregnancy	Encourage her to listen to her body; suggest that she sleep and rest as much as possible; take another walk with her
Heartburn/ indigestion	Digestion slowed by hormonal activity; pressure from enlarged uterus	Help her avoid "trouble" foods; see that she eats small meals and sips carbonated fluids

Complaint	Possible Causes	Possible Remedies
Hemorrhoids	Constipation and straining; hormonal activity strains bowel movements, dilates rectal veins	Get her off her feet, with hips raised; offer an ice pack or medicated swabs
Muscle cramp/ charley horse	Fatigue; calcium imbalance; sluggish circulation; not enough salt; pointing toes	Suggest a warm bath, give her a light massage; give her hurt muscle rapid massage; pull her foot toward her
Shooting pains	Pelvic ligaments, bones and nerves getting ready for baby	Remind her to try the Kegel exercise (when she squeezes her vaginal and rectal muscles together and then releases)
Swelling/ edema	Fluid retention (the body becomes a giant sponge)	Watch salt in her diet; offer water (not soda); suggest she lie down on left side, with legs raised on a cushion
Varicose veins	Hormone activity in muscles; excessive weight gain; heredity	Suggest she lie down on left side, with feet up; remind her not to cross her legs; suggest that she wear support stockings; watch her weight

Complaint	Possible Causes	Possible Remedies
Dizzy spells	Brain suffers decrease in oxygen-rich blood, now diverted to uterus	Sit her down quickly, put her head to her knees and get her to take deep breaths; make sure she eats regularly

to your wife's energies and capabilities. This may not be easy for you, because *your* body isn't changing—your legs don't hurt, you don't hate crowded places or the sight of most food—but you need to do it all the same. (She may well agree to let you go on alone sometimes, but don't abuse this privilege. After a while, she'll resent it.)

If morning sickness is troubling her, and friends call to invite you over for dinner, you may want to tell them about the problem to save her the embarassment of having to do so. Choose to accept only the most appealing invitations. Don't bunch up the parties back to back. Avoid stand-up cocktail parties. She will wilt, if not faint, in crowded, hot rooms. Later on, as her baby grows, she will not be able to tolerate standing for long periods.

Pregnancy Is Hard Work

Some women sail through pregnancy. Others don't. If your wife is having a difficult (though perfectly normal) pregnancy, she may not always be in a good mood. Hormonal activity and discomfort may make her ill-tempered at times and she won't necessarily keep her unhappiness to herself. Banish the myth that pregnancy is a wonderful time for her. Though she may have an easier time in subsequent pregnancies, this time it isn't much fun. If you make it clear to her that you understand that she has a hard job to do, one that *you* certainly wouldn't relish, you may find the storm clouds clearing a bit. You might even see a patch of blue.

Coping with Miscarriage

About one in five pregnancies ends in miscarriage. If early pregnancy ends abruptly, it usually means that there was a problem. Miscarriage is disappointing, but it does not prevent you from trying to get pregnant again.

Vaginal bleeding accompanied with cramps is an early sign of possible miscarriage. About a third of all women have some spotting during their pregnancy. Sometimes the bleeding is benign and the pregnancy goes to full term; at other times, the pregnancy ends within a day or two after the bleeding starts. If your wife experiences bleeding during pregnancy, notify your medical team as soon as possible, but don't be overly alarmed. She will probably be advised to rest and abstain from sexual activities.

If the bleeding stops, the pregnancy is likely to be successful: Full-term babies born after the pregnancy has been threatened by bleeding are just as likely to be normal as any other baby.

THE SHAPE OF LOVE

You may be afraid that you will lose sexual desire for your wife as her belly and breasts swell. Some fathers report that they regarded their wives as more beautiful and more exciting when full with child than they ever imagined; others found their sex life put temporarily on hold. If your sex life all but disappears during pregnancy, it doesn't mean that you have stopped loving her, and hugs and kisses can go a long way toward keeping the pilot light of your relationship going.

Pregnant women are often self-conscious about their figures. She may feel fat and awkward. She may take offense if she even suspects you have lost your desire for her. Look for ways to give her pleasure, no matter how you feel. Tell her she's beautiful. Don't tease her. It may do irreparable harm.

And if you are afraid that she may never be sexually exciting to you again, look around you. Have you ever seen so many attractive young mothers walking with their toddlers? But remember that she may need time—and help—to rekindle sexual desire after the baby is born. (There are ways to help her regain her fire; see Chapter 5.)

Sexual Love

Many couples who are pregnant for the first time find it difficult to adjust to changes in their sexual relationship. These changes interfere with your sexual access to each other and can prompt impatience, hurt and anger. So you should be absolutely clear about how the different stages of your wife's pregnancy may affect your sexual relationship with her. Know what you can do and when, and what to be careful about.

There is wide expert agreement that intercourse during pregnancy is okay and desirable. Except in particular circumstances, sex during the first two trimesters of pregnancy is safe. There is some controversy about the third trimester, with liberal voices saying that if sex feels okay, it *is* okay. If you are uncertain, consult your doctor.

Be prepared for changes in the intensity of your sexual desire and hers as you proceed through the different stages of pregnancy. In the first trimester she may not be as ardent as she was before; it's not personal, so don't take it personally. If she is sick or just plain tired, delay making love to a time when she feels like it as much as you do.

As she enters the second trimester, her stomach will settle and her energy level will perk up some. Her sexual interest also perks up as she feels better and the baby is snuggled safely in the womb. All the goings-on in the uterus have stabilized, and you'll want each other more. There's usually no reason in this period not to have sex as often as you both like.

What will also change are the sexual positions possible for you as the baby grows. The missionary position (man above, woman below) will give way to woman above, man below, or you can enter her vagina from behind while lying on your side. By the middle trimester you will need to experiment to find the best way to satisfy you both and protect the baby as well.

Lovemaking is even more tricky in the final trimester, and especially in the last few weeks before delivery. Your partner's size is one factor, and your concern for your baby's welfare is another. If you are worried about premature labor, orgasm which causes the uterus to contract may be off limits, precluding masturbation or other stimulation as well. Hugging, kissing and snuggling may be your most viable alternatives for the time being.

Togetherness

Going through your partner's pregnancy hand-in-hand with her has two parts to it. One is the opportunity to build a profoundly important bond between you. The other is your discovery of emotional depths in yourself that you probably never guessed were there.

It doesn't happen by magic. It doesn't happen without confusion, mistakes, anger, disappointment and uncertainty—on both sides. But the testimony of fathers who have consciously chosen to come to terms with pregnancy leaves no doubt that the result can also lead to a stronger, more joyful relationship. And, in the future, it will include the baby who started it all.

CHAPTER **2**

Responsibility with a Capital R

Getting through pregnancy, planning a birth and setting up the practical mechanism of family living requires that both of you learn, think and plan with care. If you have done your planning well, and have taken on the responsibility for important decisions, you will feel more at ease later on when the baby is born and needs a father. It's a shoe that will fit.

Meanwhile, back here at the beginning, let's start pulling apart the pieces that you and your partner must wrestle with. You will have to deal with surprises in a period that is neither serene nor consistent. So the more you know about what's ahead for you and your wife, the better you and she can plan and be prepared to confront contingencies with minimal fear and anxiety.

There are many important decisions to make for pregnancy, birth and baby care. To simplify that rather awesome task, here is an outline of the areas to focus on as you go along.

1. What tasks around the house need doing and who should do them?

_____ Laundry	_____ Vacuuming
_____ Grocery shopping	_____ Clean kitchen
_____ Cooking	_____ Clean bathroom(s)
_____ Dishes	_____ Errands
_____ Lawn-mowing and gardening	_____ Special Projects

2. How involved do you want and expect to be in the birth of this baby?

_____ Participate in selection of obstetrical medical team

_____ Participate in selection of a suitable birth environment

_____ Accompany wife on prenatal checkups

_____ Participate in decision about prenatal testing

_____ Attend childbirth education classes to prepare for coaching role

_____ Practice labor breathing techniques with wife during pregnancy

3. How involved do you want and expect to be in nurturing your baby?

_____ Shop for nursery furniture, car seat and baby clothes

_____ Attend parenting preparation class for tips on taking care of the baby

_____ Participate in the selection of the baby's doctor

_____ Participate in making the decision between breast-feeding and bottle-feeding

4. What financial planning does your new family need?

____ Decide how you are going to pay for prenatal care, childbirth and postpartum care

____ Plan weekly or monthly budget for your family's income after the baby is born

Each area in the list above offers you opportunities to become actively involved in adapting your life to the new baby. When you and your partner form a consensus as to what you want and how you get it, there will be fewer surprises. You will be less likely to say, "I wish we could have..." or "Why did we...?"

As you and your wife tackle each section, read up on the subject and talk to those who in your judgment have handled the situation well. Seek out several experts to get more than one or two opinions. To get you started, in this chapter we will discuss each of the areas in turn and try to help you do what is best for you and your family.

Household Help

Start by thinking small, on a domestic scale. Even though you are exultant at this turn of events ("Wow! I'm going to be a father!"), down on the ground, where you live, the house still has to be cleaned, dishes washed, meals prepared, laundry done, food provided. As a philosopher once said, life is made up of one damned thing after another. They add up.

How you handle chores is a choice as individual as you and your partner. Paid help is one solution, great if you can afford it. If not, improvise your own plan that clearly states who does what. Assuming that your partner works, you're probably already sharing the chores and have a head start. Make a list of the chores, pare them down to the most essential ones, and take on as many yourself as you reasonably can. Some jobs can be delayed or reassigned.

TIP: *Don't strive for a 50-50 balance. The fair balance, given the circumstances, may turn out to be 75-25, with your shoulders carrying the heavier load. Remember, your wife's body is undergoing changes during pregnancy and she won't be able to do the bending, stooping and lifting of heavy housework. (When she has to bend over, make sure she squats without bending her back.)*

Being There

Many men don't know if they want to be present during labor and childbirth, nor do they feel immediately confident about taking on the role of labor coach. It's an uncertain, intimidating experience. You may not feel ready. The task covers new, untried ground. There are so many questions you won't be able to answer beforehand:

- Will I vomit?
- Will I faint at the sight of blood?
- Can I face seeing the woman I love in pain and distress?
- As I've never done this before, will I just be in the way? Will I fail?

All these are legitimate questions. Though there are no certain ways to discover how you will handle childbirth before labor starts, there are ways to test your mettle: Watch the film on birth in a childbirth class and see how you react to the scenes. Think back to how you reacted in an emergency situation (any kind of emergency, not just a medical alert). Did you keep your wits about you? Your reactions in these circumstances will help you determine how you will weather childbirth.

You can further allay your fears by asking questions in prepared childbirth class (see page 37). Talk with other fathers in the class. You will discover that you are all sharing the same misgivings and self-doubts. You will soon learn that you are all sailing in the same boat.

If it is possible for you to be present at your baby's birth, it's worth a try. The worst that can happen is that you will have to leave. Later, if you feel better, you can return. But if you don't try, you'll never know (1) if you could have done it, (2) any part of your wife's experience, and (3) the first minutes of your baby's life.

Chances are that you will rise above yourself. Your weak stomach will be overruled by the importance of the moment. If the sight of the placenta or a certain medical procedure is distasteful, look away. By viewing childbirth films you can learn to anticipate what you don't want to see.

Just as you have been there from the beginning, you are also a key player during childbirth. Take part and be involved. You are needed to assist at your baby's birth. Your wife definitely cannot do it alone.

Your Birth Plan

A birth plan is the matrix of decisions that surrounds a labor and birth. What kind of atmosphere and medical trappings do you want for your birth experience? How much medical

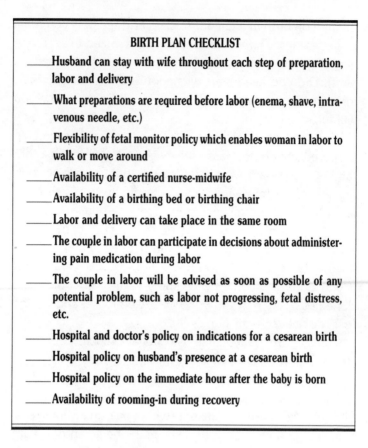

BIRTH PLAN CHECKLIST

_____Husband can stay with wife throughout each step of preparation, labor and delivery

_____What preparations are required before labor (enema, shave, intravenous needle, etc.)

_____Flexibility of fetal monitor policy which enables woman in labor to walk or move around

_____Availability of a certified nurse-midwife

_____Availability of a birthing bed or birthing chair

_____Labor and delivery can take place in the same room

_____The couple in labor can participate in decisions about administering pain medication during labor

_____The couple in labor will be advised as soon as possible of any potential problem, such as labor not progressing, fetal distress, etc.

_____Hospital and doctor's policy on indications for a cesarean birth

_____Hospital policy on husband's presence at a cesarean birth

_____Hospital policy on the immediate hour after the baby is born

_____Availability of rooming-in during recovery

intervention do you want in the labor and birth process? Some procedures may be optional, like the intravenous needle; others, like the fetal monitor, are mandatory in hospitals. Other questions to consider in formulating a birth plan: When do we opt for pain medication? What can we do if a cesarean birth becomes a real possibility?

TIP: *When formulating a birth plan or scenario for labor and delivery, keep in mind that there is no way to predict exactly what will happen or how your wife will react to it. You and your wife need to think about contingencies. Learn to phrase these sentences with "If . . ., then . . . ."*

Hospital, Doctor, Nurse-Midwife

Hospitals vary widely in what they offer. You will have to do some homework to discover the facilities in your area that fit your needs and wants. Some offer family-centered birth experiences; some are sterile and impersonal. Others fall somewhere in the middle.

These days, hospitals are trying to get your business. Some woo pregnant couples with so-called Maternity Teas, where hospital policies and programs are explained and prizes given out. Gone are the old days of dry maternity tours. They want you. You can pick and choose.

Birth Centers

Alternative birth centers or ABCs, also called maternity centers, are stand-alone facilities which offer full prenatal, birth, newborn and postpartum services. They are designed for the medically low-risk woman (typically, a healthy woman in her 20s), and your wife would be in the care of a Certified Nurse-Midwife (see page 40), with staff obstetricians and pediatricians as backup. ABCs offer the professionalism of a hospital in an environment that encourages both partners to be actively involved in the birth of their baby.

As yet there are no uniform licensing criteria or standards set up for these centers. Each is different and may or

---

WHAT IS A BIRTHING BED?

A birthing bed, unlike the beds in a labor room, can accommodate your wife's labor and the actual birth of the baby. If she labors in a traditional bed, she will have to be moved to another room at a crucial moment: the onset of the second stage of labor (see Chapter 3, page 54).

The birthing bed can be adjusted during labor and childbirth to give your wife a more upright and comfortable position during labor and delivery, which tends to speed each stage of childbirth. An upright posture enables her to enlist the aid of gravity when pushing the baby out, rather than lying flat on a delivery table with her legs in stirrups.

---

may not meet quality-of-care and safety standards. ABCs are still few and far between. Most of them are located on the east and west coasts, usually in heavily populated areas, although they can be found scattered lightly across the country. For information, write or call The Cooperative Birth Center Network (Box 1, Route 1, Perkiomenville, PA 18074; 215-234-8068).

Childbirth Education

One of the best places to get answers to many of your questions is your childbirth education class. These are classes you attend with your wife when she is in her seventh month of pregnancy. Once a week, the instructor will teach you and your partner breathing, relaxation and psychological techniques to cope with the pain of labor contractions. You will see a film of a birth and go step by step through the processes of labor, delivery and recovery.

Prepared childbirth methods travel under a variety of titles—Dick-Read's *Childbirth Without Fear* approach, the Lamaze method (the most popular in this country), Sheila Kitzinger's psychosexual theory and Dr. Robert Bradley's husband-coached childbirth are among the best known. There has also been some use of acupuncture and hypnotherapy, but they are not so much methods of natural childbirth as forms of natural anesthesia, because they do not rely on chemicals for their effects.

These methods fall into one of two categories. The psy-

WHY PREPARED CHILDBIRTH?

- To educate parents-to-be about birth, the stages of labor and the nature of contractions in each stage, so that they both know what to expect
- To give control over the birth process to the one person, the mother-to-be, to whom it rightfully belongs
- To break the fear-tension-pain reaction to labor contractions by a variety of methods, including breathing, relaxation and concentration techniques
- To teach physical exercises to condition the woman for the work of labor and delivery
- To prepare the labor coach for his role in the birth
- To inform parents about hospital policies, parents' rights and options, and comfort measures in labor, including pain medication

---

TYPICAL MEDICAL PROCEDURES DURING LABOR AND CHILDBIRTH

Type	Function
Intravenous needle	Allows woman to receive glucose solution directly into her system, which keeps her from becoming dehydrated during labor, and to receive pain medication if indicated
Enema	Empties the bowel to eliminate pressure on the birth canal; often optional
Pubic shave	Hair around immediate area of episiotomy (see below) is shaved or clipped
Episiotomy	The incision(s) that enlarges the vaginal opening to accommodate the baby's head at birth and prevents tearing of tissues; may be optional
Fetal monitor	An external or internal monitor which records the frequency and length of the contractions and tracks the baby's heartbeat; it attaches externally with straps or belts around the woman's abdomen, or attaches internally via a tiny electrode to the baby's head; seldom optional

choprophylactic school, with Lamaze at the head, seeks to deflect pain and teaches pain control through breathing, relaxation and distraction of the woman in labor. Lamaze philosophy requires a labor coach to support and encourage the laboring woman, focusing on each contraction as it comes.

The proponents of the latter school differ in emphasis but all rely on creating a positive psychological state to break the fear-tension-pain cycle so common in labor. The woman in labor learns to tune in to the baby and the physical process of birth as her body responds, using breathing and concentration techniques.

Your wife is in training just as an athlete is dedicated to conditioning his or her body. In class you will learn to simulate a contraction: A typical exercise is for you to pinch her—hard—on the knee or heel with increasing pressure while she practices using her breathing techniques to ignore the pain. We encourage you to practice daily as training will enable her to reduce, or even eliminate altogether, her need for pain-killing drugs. Get in the habit of breathing with her. Help her learn to relax her muscles and her thoughts. These sessions will get you in the habit of being her cheerleader and coach for the marathon ahead. You'll be ready!

Professional Help

One of the best sources of reassurance and support is the doctor or certified nurse-midwife you enlist for your prenatal care and childbirth. Your goal is to choose someone who can endorse your birth plan. Depending on the community where you live, this may not be possible. Your fall-back position is to find a doctor who has persuasive reasons for where he or she disagrees with you and is willing to discuss them with you both as adults, not as an all-wise teacher dealing with stubborn, ignorant children.

Try to avoid, of course, adopting a similar attitude toward the doctors you meet. You and your partner may be extremely well informed and feel confident in your opinions, but these are not the same as medical experience and professional judgment. It may be necessary to make compromises in order to assure your wife's safety and a successful delivery.

There's another reason for shopping around: the high and steadily rising cost of medical care. Only those with excellent medical insurance can ignore the doctor's fee in making a selection. This should be explicitly discussed at the outset.

The Certified Nurse-Midwife (CNM) Alternative

Many couples these days are looking closely at professionals other than a doctor to provide routine prenatal care and attend their labor and delivery. The certified nurse-midwife is a viable alternative for low-risk pregnancies without medical complications. A CNM is a professional registered nurse who has completed an educational program on pregnancy, birth and the postpartum period and has passed national certification boards. CNMs are affiliated with a physician in private practice, a hospital or a health maintenance organization. They consult with physicians in the event of any medical problems, and will turn a case over to the physician if advisable.

A certified nurse-midwife sees pregnancy and childbirth as a natural experience. The great advantage of having a CNM on your team is that he or she will stay with your wife through each contraction and give you expert help while you coach her. CNMs also have expertise in being advocates for the laboring couple, whose preferences may not be top priority for busy, overworked hospital staff. If you would like information on who is available in your area, write to the American College of Nurse-Midwives (1522 K Street, NW, Suite 1120, Washington, D.C. 20005).

Other Decisions: Tests During Pregnancy

SONOGRAMS

Ultrasound screening, like radar, bounces waves off the fetus and then translates the results into dots on a screen. This is a relatively new technology, and there is disagreement among professionals about the safety of the test for routine pregnancies. Little is known about long-term effects on the baby. Before allowing a test to be performed, be certain that there is a sound medical reason for administering it. If there is, the odds are good that the information it gives the doctor will outweigh the possible risks to the baby.

AMNIOCENTESIS AND CVS

Amniocentesis is recommended for women over 35 to flag fetuses with chromosomal abnormalities such as Down's syndrome. A woman must wait 15 to 19 weeks after conception to have the test done. A needle is inserted carefully (using a sonogram to guide the technician) into the amniotic sac that cushions the baby while in the uterus. A small amount of amniotic fluid is withdrawn and cultured in a lab for two to six weeks. The technique has been perfected over the years, but still carries a low risk of miscarriage.

A new chromosomal test, Chorionic Villus Sampling, or CVS, is just being approved by the Food and Drug Administration. As of this writing only a large handful of institutions are authorized by the government to perform this probable successor to amniocentesis. If the test continues to be successful, more and more institutions will be allowed to use it.

CVS can be done as early as the eighth week after conception. Using a sonogram as a guide, the technician inserts a flexible plastic catheter through the vagina into the cervix. A small piece of the chorion (the early placenta which supports the baby with nutrients and oxygen) is removed. Because chorion cells are actively growing when removed and require no culturing, test results are ready in about a week.

Women experience no pain and the test can be completed in 15 minutes or so. So far the only women who are advised not to have the test are those who are susceptible to miscarriage or who have experienced bleeding during their pregnancy.

NOTE: Positive results from either test require the couple to make an intensely personal decision about whether the pregnancy should be allowed to continue.

Choosing a Doctor for Your Baby

Your medical adviser is a good source of names. Ask friends you trust, too. Sometimes one or two names will keep reappearing. This is both good and bad: The doctor is probably overworked and too busy for the extra attention you may feel you want, but he or she may also offer the best care in town.

In metropolitan areas, it is an accepted practice to interview pediatricians before the baby is born. Personal interviews will help assure you that you are making the best choice. Comparing your notes and impressions, you and your wife can settle on someone who fits your needs. In smaller communities, word of mouth and referrals are your only resources.

Choose a pediatrician who:
- is conveniently located.
- is affiliated with the hospital you prefer.
- has convenient calling hours (for those small, but important questions that all new parents ask).
- has partners or backup doctors whom you trust.
- if your wife plans to nurse your baby, supports breast-feeding wholeheartedly (not all pediatricians do).
- is up-to-date on the latest pediatric trends and findings.
- will be on hand in the hospital to examine the baby within 24 hours after birth.

Baby Accessories

Before the baby comes, you will need to buy or borrow a crib and, if you have a car, a car safety seat.

A crib should be sturdy and stable, have short corner posts (knobs are hazardous), and have adjustable mattress levels, so that you can lower the mattress as the baby grows. If you are considering a secondhand crib, whether purchased or borrowed, make sure that none of the pieces is missing and that the crib slats are no more than $2\frac{3}{8}$ inches apart so that your baby's head cannot get caught in between them.

Whether you are buying an infant seat, a convertible seat (which can be adjusted for an infant or a toddler), or a toddler safety seat, it should meet the requirements of Federal Motor Vehicle Safety Standard 213, be easy to use, and must fit in your car without obstructing your rear view.

NAMING YOUR BABY

The name you give your baby is important and should be considered carefully. Here are a few guidelines to keep in mind:

- If you are going to give the baby your name or that of your wife, plan how you are going to avoid confusion (i.e., by using a nickname for him or her).
- Look at your last name. Is it hard to spell or pronounce? If so, choose a common first name.
- Remember that the first name will sound better with the last name if each has a different number of syllables.
- Do you like the nicknames associated with the name?
- Are there any hidden or slang meanings to the name?
- What will the initials be on his shirt or her briefcase?
- Depending on the gender, would you or your wife be proud to have the name?

Books of possible names (there's one in this series, too) can help you find just the right one for *your* baby

It is extremely important to install the seat properly; if it is improperly installed, the seat will be less safe for your baby.

> IMPORTANT SAFETY TIP: *Make a habit of using the safety seat every time you drive anywhere with the baby. A seat that isn't used won't protect your baby.*

Financial Planning

There are many additional expenses to squeeze into your budget during these months before your baby comes. Unless you have someone to give you what you need for your baby, you will have to invest in other nursery furniture as well as the crib, something to carry the baby in (a cloth carrier, stroller or carriage) as well as a safety seat for traveling in the car—and, of course, baby clothes and other necessities.

Your wife will have additional expenses to safeguard her health and the baby's during her pregnancy and after the baby is born. She will need vitamin supplements while she is pregnant and if she breast-feeds. The costs can be as much as $75 a month and possibly higher.

She will need more frequent dental checkups, too. Because of hormonal changes in a pregnant woman's body, her gums can become exceedingly sensitive and develop an unhealthy appearance, bleeding readily during brushing or flossing. Professional cleaning every three months or even once a month during pregnancy may be necessary to control the condition. Plan for the cost. Health insurance plans that include dental care are still uncommon.

Insurance, Or It's More Fun to Read the Phone Book

Unless you habitually read the documents that control your destiny, such as the lease on your apartment, the terms of your home mortgage and your credit card contract, you probably don't know the extent of your medical insurance coverage. Though reading insurance documents is slow going, it is also very important. As soon as possible, set aside time to scrutinize your policy.

Look for what it *doesn't* include. Deductibles are steadily rising, "comprehensive" may not mean what it says, and obstetric (and related maternity costs) and well-baby care are *not* covered in many policies. Read the small print, the footnotes, the provisos. Every word in an insurance policy counts. Don't confuse hospital coverage with medical/surgical coverage.

To penetrate the professional jargon on your own may

seem like a forbidding task, and you may be tempted to take a lot for granted. Press on. Ask around. It's not unlikely that a friend has already broken the code and can either interpret your policy for you, or can at least help you with the language.

Many books and publications also translate the special terminology of insurance policies into understandable language. And you have a perfect right to go to your carrier's representative and request information.

If your wife is covered by your policy at work and her own employee coverage as well, watch out for dual coverage. The overlap can sometimes result in waivers or restrictive conditions.

HMO: An Insurance Alternative

A health maintenance organization (HMO) is a community of doctors and other medical specialists, often including laboratory and radiology services. They provide continuous medical care to their members, with all the auxiliary services needed along the way, for a fixed, prepaid monthly fee. They dissolve the traditional equation that kept medical insurers on one side and the professionals who deliver the health care on the other. Both are in the same shop.

Having joined one, you, your partner and the baby after arrival receive virtually unlimited medical care for the monthly fee. This is pay-as-you-go care available under conventional health insurance policies.

Sounds too good to be true, you figure, and there has to be a catch, like huge fees for such a comprehensive service without the exclusions, limitations, deductions and "reasonable and customary" fee restrictions typical in standard policies?

Not so. A number of studies have shown that HMO premiums are lower than those of traditional insurers while, most important, benefits are much broader. Increasing costs continue to boost fees in both camps, but the evidence suggests that HMO premiums are rising about half as fast as those of old-line health insurance companies.

But the money you save at an HMO may not be worth it, because it may not offer the important emotional support and confidence that a one-on-one relationship with a private practitioner often provides. HMOs operate under a kind of anonymity, or impersonality. HMOs are communal institutions and doctors are, in a very real sense, interchangeable. Thus your wife may not have the opportunity to develop the trusting, supportive relationship with a doctor that is so stabilizing during the often anxious, uncertain months of pregnancy. You and she may prize the relationship with her medical adviser, and feel there's no substitute for his or her intimate knowledge of the pregnancy.

With an HMO you can't choose which doctor you have.

There's no guarantee, for example, that your wife will always see the same obstetrician during her pregnancy; moreover, childbirth will be attended by the obstetrician who is on duty at the hospital. So, you and your wife may not be familiar with this doctor at a very sensitive and vulnerable moment in your lives. (A non-HMO team of obstetricians also rotates duty on nights and weekends, so if your baby is born outside regular business hours, you may not get your own doctor in that case either.)

Because of the payment system, HMO doctors are inclined to be sensitive to costs and can be cautious in calling for treatment that may skew the unit's budget. HMOs, even those that are non-profit, are not philanthropies; they have to control expenses. This can mean that a decision may not be made until the doctors agree that a proposed treatment is, in fact, both the most economical and the most effective.

Ready and Eager

In this chapter we have approached pregnancy as a period of decisions for both you and your wife. As it draws to a close, you will feel better prepared—on paper, at least—for labor and childbirth. Working together on all these crucial matters will make you both eager for the future to arrive.

"Together"—that's the magic word.

CHAPTER 3

Labor and Birth

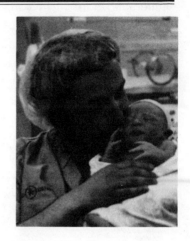

During the last months of pregnancy your role as ally and friend to your wife is particularly important. By acting as coach-advocate during pregnancy and childbirth and, later after the baby is born, nurturing the baby as well as providing for him, you will become a family man in the truest sense.

If you roll up your sleeves and plunge into the fathering experience, you will be repaid a thousand times. It's value added all the way, both for you and for your wife. By working with her to manage the pain of childbirth and by witnessing the birth of your baby, you'll be on the inside of an event so momentous that it defies description.

Fathers, in the attempt to attach words to it, try "awe," "amazement," "reborn" (themselves), "overcome," and report feeling a rush of love for their wives that exceeded any emotion they had ever experienced.

When you reach the end of this chapter you will be holding your baby—at least in your imagination. An amazing thought indeed. But before you and your wife get to that moment, there's the task of labor and childbirth to get through. It is our intent to show you that it isn't as overwhelming as it may at first seem. Like any big project, you start at the beginning, take it step by step, and before you know it, it's done.

Whose Baby Is It Anyway?

You and your wife should approach childbirth with a completely clean slate, no received opinions. As you explore your options you will find abundant opportunities to share in an event that, in the truest sense, belongs to her and you alone.

Indeed, you can do much to strengthen that critical sense of ownership by thinking in terms of "giving birth." "Delivery" is a term that pushes the parents, chiefly the mother-to-be, off center stage and suggests that the medical team are the principal players. But the fact is that, however indispensable they may be in complicated or emergency situations, they are outsiders in this main event of your life, and you will not depreciate their contribution by regarding them as such. You and your wife have the power to retain control of this landmark moment in your life together.

LABOR AND CHILDBIRTH: AN OVERVIEW

You'll be better able to support your wife through labor to the birth of your baby if you know the phases of childbirth and how each affects her. Here's a quick overview plus some practical suggestions about how you can help.

"Labor" is a well-chosen word assigned to the efforts a woman's body makes to force the baby out of the uterus (womb) into the world. A series of contractions, not unlike the regular flexing of biceps, increases in frequency, duration and intensity until the baby is born. This is called labor because it is hard work—very hard work. In fact, it is a marathon of truly Olympian proportions.

As we have said, there is no way to predict what your wife's first labor will be like. In subsequent pregnancies her first experience may be a general guide to what will occur—but surprises may happen. Like the proverbial Boy Scout: Be prepared.

The Stages of Childbirth

THE FIRST STAGE

The work of the first stage is the flattening or effacement and the opening up of the cervix (the mouth of the uterus) to ten centimeters, also described as "five fingers." This is the longest stage, lasting on average from 12 to 18 hours.

As the cervix dilates, your wife must cope with increasingly intense assaults of pain. As her labor coach, you must help her to combat the fear and tension that severe pain creates. Tenderness and encouragement will help her to relax and to brave the next contraction and the one after that.

THE ONSET OF LABOR

Because the early contractions are mild, usually no more intense than premenstrual cramps, it isn't always clear that true labor has started. Indeed, women sometimes experience false labor which has contractions that are similar to those of "true" labor. The difference lies in their irregularity and the fact that they go away when the woman moves around. If the membranes of the amniotic sac rupture, also called "the waters breaking," there is no doubt that labor has begun. *But remember: True labor can begin with the amniotic sac intact.* Once the bag of water breaks, contractions may increase in intensity and efficiency.

When the clear amniotic fluid gushes out, it happens without warning (unless your birth attendant decides to puncture the bag artificially—a speedy and completely painless procedure). Because the fluid comes through the vaginal opening, there is no way to hold it back until a toilet is handy. The only way to prepare for it is for your wife to line your bed with a waterproof sheet and keep a thick bath towel handy wherever she goes (in the family car, a shopping bag, or the grocery cart, etc.).

The first stage can be divided into three parts, each of which is successively shorter in duration:

Conversational Phase: The cervix dilates from one to four centimeters. As the name implies, this is the least intense phase, with contractions coming six to 15 minutes apart. You should alert your medical team and follow their instructions about when to go to the hospital.

Active Phase: The cervix dilates from four to seven

centimeters. Pain is more intense now, with contractions coming every three to five minutes.

Transition: The cervix dilates from seven to ten centimeters. Pain is at its peak, with contractions coming every 90 seconds. There may only be a rest of 30 seconds between the end of one contraction and the onset of the next.

TIP: *If your watch has a stop-watch function or a second hand, use it to help her time the contractions. When you are timing contractions, mark the intervals from the beginning of one to the beginning of the next one.*

THE SECOND STAGE

Your wife enters this stage when she has dilated the full ten centimeters and is encouraged by the medical team to push. The baby descends into the birth canal and is born. The baby moves out of the uterus, turns to face nose down (facing your partner's spine) and inches past the tailbone and pubic bone. If the baby's head turns properly, this stage is usually not particularly painful. If the baby has difficulties maneuvering through the passage, this stage can be quite prolonged.

If your wife has been in a traditional labor room, she will be moved to the delivery room. Once she is on the delivery table, either you or a labor nurse will need to help her elevate her upper torso so she can get a good angle for bearing down during contractions. As before, she will rest between contractions.

THE THIRD STAGE

Your wife pushes out the placenta or afterbirth. Until now the placenta has been the life support system that brings

BACK LABOR

If the baby is facing away from your wife's spine and is "sunny side up," the head presses on her tailbone, causing severe back labor pain.

The good news is that you can relieve much of her discomfort by applying strong, constant counterpressure to her lower back and buttocks. Pressing tennis balls or a wallpaper roller against her (she'll direct you where) saves your arms from giving out.

fresh blood containing nutrients and oxygen to the baby and removes the waste from the baby's circulation. Now it is no longer needed and it disengages from the uterus. This process usually lasts only a short time, with a few mild contractions needed to push it out. To encourage its expulsion, a labor nurse may massage or push on her abdomen. Keep in mind that during this phase, your baby has already been born. Your mind—as well as your wife's—is occupied with your new baby. This stage occurs without much conscious effort or attention.

The Power of Two

The word "coach" has its origins on the athletic playing fields of America. The image is clear: She is the athlete with a marathon to win; you are the trainer, dedicated to her success. As an athlete must train for an event, she must practice endlessly. She must condition her muscles and condition her behavior. You, as her trainer, are actively involved in making sure that she is ready.

```
┌─────────────────────────────────────────────────────┐
│                                                       │
│        A LABOR COACH KIT TO BRING TO THE HOSPITAL     │
│   • This book                                         │
│   • Newspapers, magazines and a favorite book to read aloud if labor │
│     is slow                                           │
│   • A radio or tape player with favorite tapes        │
│   • Quick energy snacks for you                       │
│   • A razor, toothbrush, and clean shirt              │
│   • Address book and change for pay phone             │
│   • A camera loaded with film                         │
│                                                       │
│   For her comfort:                                    │
│                                                       │
│   • A favorite pillow                                 │
│   • Lip balm, talcum powder, body lotion              │
│   • Tennis balls or a wallpaper roller for counterpressure │
│   • Lollipops                                         │
│                                                       │
└─────────────────────────────────────────────────────┘
```

Then, when the time comes, you are committed to her throughout the ordeal. You must concentrate with her through every contraction. But there is a good deal more to it than the mental energy involved. You can really help her.

Don't underestimate the power of massage and counter-pressure for back labor. Any other comfort measures you can offer will make a big difference to her morale. Don't expect much in the way of "please" and "thank you." She probably won't be able to do much more than grunt or moan her appreciation.

As labor progresses, she will be less able to ask for what she needs or wants. When that happens, you will be in the position of having to take an educated guess as to what to do for her. By that time you will have already logged in several hours and you'll probably know what works and what she wants.

Finally, let's say a word about how *you* are going to get through all those hours in labor. When you are on the outside looking in, it may be hard to imagine taking on a job that is so intense and that takes such a long time to finish. But when she's laboring with concentration, time, in

HOW A LABOR COACH CAN HELP

Here are some specifics that you can do to get her through the long hours of labor. Keep this list with you in labor as a reminder.

- Massage her back muscles till your own arms ache.
- Offer her ice chips.
- Breathe or chant with her.
- Read to her or talk idly to pass the time.
- Rally her morale with a pep talk.
- Time her contractions so she knows how far she has to go before she can rest again.
- Adjust the pillows or birthing bed.
- Help her change positions.
- Walk her around to speed up a sluggish labor.
- Press tennis balls or a wallpaper roller against her back and buttocks to provide counterpressure against back labor.
- In the last stage of dilation, help her resist the urge to push.
- Elevate her upper torso when she must push the baby and the afterbirth out.

CATCH 22: CESAREAN BIRTH

A cesarean birth is abdominal surgery that is performed in a regular operating room for various reasons: Fetal distress (stress to the baby caused by a lack of oxygen during labor), lack of progress during labor, and a previous cesarean birth are common causes. (These days, more and more doctors are willing, in certain circumstances, to allow a woman to labor and experience vaginal childbirth despite a previous cesarean birth.) Anatomical reasons are often cited as well: The baby may be too big or the mother's pelvis may be too small.

If there is a physical reason that is determined before labor begins (you may want to have another doctor give a second opinion on the subject), your wife will be able to make an appointment for surgery. If your wife has epidural anesthesia (a local), she will be awake during delivery, and depending on hospital policy, you may be permitted into the operating room.

Many cesareans are performed after labor has begun and there isn't always time for a local anesthetic to be administered. In cases such as these, a general anesthetic is used and fathers are not usually allowed into the operating room.

This fact underscores the importance of contingency planning. One decision can lead to another in a chain of events. Consider carefully the course you take. But even careful planning cannot ensure that the road during childbirth won't take an unexpected turn. Even the best laid plans can backfire.

One birth in five is cesarean. If your childbirth education class has ten couples in it, two are likely to have a cesarean birth. You look around the room at all these pregnant women and think, "It won't be us." But you never know. It's as likely to be you as anyone else.

Note: If your wife does have a cesarean, and especially if she has a general anesthetic, be prepared for her to have a slower and more uncomfortable recovery period after the baby is born. Your support and understanding will go a long way to help.

effect, stands still. If you are concentrating with her and are actively involved in alleviating her pain, you too will be only vaguely aware of the clock.

Waiting for the Stork

There is nothing magic about a due date. Even if it was calculated accurately, using the correct date for the beginning of the last period, and your wife's menstrual cycle is regular, the baby still may come at any time two weeks before or after the actual day. So you will be kept guessing—which is excellent training for parenting later on!

As the countdown begins, you will stick close to the phone. You'll be reluctant to take a long lunch hour and anxious if you become stuck somewhere in traffic. If the due date comes and goes, your nerves will start to fray. If she has false labor (contractions that are erratic and disappear if she moves around), tempers may become even thinner. Try not to be so anxious. Remember: Once your baby comes, he'll stay.

If there is reason to believe that your wife's pregnancy has been prolonged past 42 weeks or that the placenta is not functioning properly, your medical team will probably induce her labor. Her amniotic sac may be broken first, and then she may be given the drug oxytocin in an intravenous needle. Another catalyst for labor is the synthetic hormone prostaglandin, administered as a suppository, gel or tablet.

TIP: *If her labor does not start spontaneously, and the medical team induces labor, she will skip the easy-going early phase of labor and have intense contractions right from the start.*

Ready, Set, Go!

CONVERSATIONAL PHASE

If labor starts in the evening or the middle of the night, you should both try to rest. You have a long haul ahead of you and you will be better for facing it refreshed. Early labor is not particularly uncomfortable. It is more likely that excitement rather than pain will prevent sleep. Once you're sure that true labor has started, her diet must be restricted to a little clear liquid like broth or sugar tea. You should follow the recommendation of your medical team. You, of course, can chow down, if you feel like it—but do it discreetly!

Follow your medical adviser's instructions as to when to alert your medical team. Most physicians and certified nurse-midwives want to know when the contractions are steadily coming about ten to 12 minutes apart, or when her water breaks, with or without contractions. Any unusual or painful discomforts should be reported as well.

ACTIVE PHASE

As labor progresses and contractions intensify, she loses her ability to carry on a conversation and communicates her needs with grunts and moans. You must help her to relax, conserve her energy and stay confident. As the going gets rougher, all three become increasingly difficult.

Here is when the routine practice of the past weeks pays off. Anxiety and tension are the enemies, for they act to undermine her control of the situation. "You can do it, you can do it," is an effective chant for some coaches. Your demonstration of total confidence in her, of your support and attention, are the greatest contributions you can make.

A few words of caution. In the beginning of labor (when the cervix dilates to four centimeters), the spirits of expectant parents run high. There is excitement because the long-awaited event is finally at hand, and discomfort is minimal.

As labor intensifies, the fun stops and serious business begins. Anticipation fades. An invisible wall goes up around the laboring woman. She seems remote and will show little recognition or appreciation of the efforts you're making on her behalf. She can't. The contractions, coming more quickly and intensely now, absorb all her energy. She hears you. She knows what you're doing, but she can't make the effort to tell you so. All her resources are concentrated on her contractions and resting in between them.

TRANSITION

This is the crescendo and usually mercifully short, lasting an hour or two. Contractions are coming fast and are at the height of intensity. She has almost no time to rest. Indeed, she may doze during the 30 to 45 seconds of rest time between, and wake to another 60 to 90 seconds of contraction. The fact that she dozes between contractions helps to sustain her during this difficult phase, but it is also hard on her because whenever she is awake, she is having a contraction.

Women react variously to the pain of this process. A few remain quiet, but many become angry, impatient and short-tempered. It is important to remember not to take it personally. Now's the time for encouraging words, even if she is swearing a blue streak. It's a great sign! Alert the staff to be ready because you're almost there.

PUSHING

When the nurse-midwife or physician determines that she is fully dilated, she will get the go-ahead to push. This is a relief for many women. She can give in to the urge to push, and the pressure she exerts when bearing down is likely to erase the pain felt during earlier contractions. (As we mentioned earlier, however, if the baby doesn't rotate, she will be in as much pain, if not more pain, than she was in transition.) She is no longer passively getting through, she is actively engaged. Pushing is hard work. It may last a half hour or several hours. Give her frequent progress reports as the head appears and then disappears between contractions (your partner's eyes close with the effort of pushing; she won't see it).

TIP: *As she enters the second stage there will be moments when she can't bear down when she has the urge to do so: When she is being transferred to the delivery table and when the episiotomy incision is being performed are two points when she* must *resist her impulse to push. If she has been practicing controlling these muscles by doing her childbirth exercises, these efforts will pay off now. Help her stay in control by encouraging her to relax and breathing with her during these crucial periods.*

At Last!

And then that moment comes that you and your partner have worked over for many months. The baby's head crowns, your baby's hair is visible. The vision you see is hypnotizing. Wake up! If you have brought a camera along, have it at the ready to take pictures.

Soon the head clears the vaginal opening and the shoulders follow. A moment later the baby slips out. Shortly afterward, you are holding a new creature in your arms. Your baby! He is truly beautiful. It doesn't matter that he is blue, wrinkled and still covered with packing material. It doesn't matter that he looks like Jonathan Winters. He has changed your life forever. Things come and go, but you will always be this child's daddy. You have entered into fatherhood, stage one.

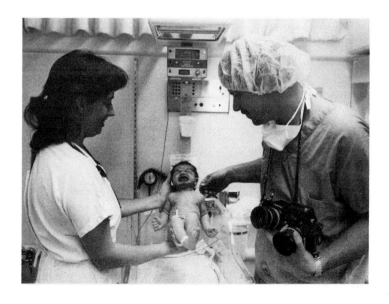

CHAPTER **4**

Real Men Are Daddies

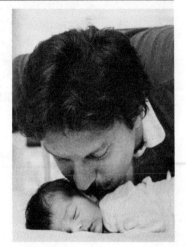

The Baby's First Hours

Amazingly, after the ordeal of birth, the baby is quietly alert, ready to start puzzling out the new world she has fallen into. She will remain so for about an hour before she drifts off to sleep. This first hour can be a special time for you and your wife to get to know your baby.

If there have been no special complications in childbirth, the two of you will be left for awhile with your baby before she is taken off to the nursery. Take turns holding the baby. Your wife may be feeling shaky and need you to support her arm while she holds the baby. If she is going to breast-feed, she may want to put the baby to her breast.

If your wife has had a cesarean birth or if circumstances don't permit the initial hour together, don't worry. Whenever it is that you begin holding and nurturing your baby, you will still cover the same ground. Hours, days and weeks lie ahead full of opportunities for you to get to know one another.

A New, Improved You

When your baby is born and you finally leave the room where it happened, you will certainly feel tired and relieved. And you may also discover a tangible difference in the way you see yourself and the rest of the world. You may feel stronger and more capable than ever before.

You may be so excited and proud of your baby that you can't wait to show her off. Seeing, holding and touching her are bound to be exhilarating experiences. In fact, you may feel that this is the greatest baby in the whole history of the world!

If you have been able to enjoy your baby during the first hour after birth, you may decide to go home for some well-deserved rest. Or your system may still be charged with excitement and you may want to remain. Your baby will usually be transferred to the nursery and your wife will be moved either to a recovery room or her own hospital bed. You may find yourself shuttling back and forth with up-to-the-minute status reports. If your wife is as supercharged with excitement as you are, you will probably want to share the experience with the only other person in the world who can appreciate it.

Don't worry if you aren't so ecstatic. Circumstances and personality determine how a man reacts to the drama of birth. Becoming a father is subject to all the variables and uncertainties inherent in human nature. It is hard to predict exactly how you will feel. Don't anticipate or force how you feel. Be patient. Give yourself time to experience your baby. You'll enjoy it more if you don't attach pre-established expectations to the enjoyment.

Hospital Miscellany

ROOMING-IN

If the hospital allows rooming-in, i.e., allows your baby to be in the hospital room with you and your wife for all or part of the day, and if your wife feels up to it, it is a great

---

WHAT HAPPENS IMMEDIATELY AFTER BIRTH

Mother:	Baby:
Nurse massages uterus externally	Cord clamped and cut
Local anesthetic is administered and episiotomy sewn up (with stitches that will gradually dissolve)	Nose and throat suctioned
	Weighed, cleaned and footprinted
Sucks on lollipop or ice chips and rests	Eye drops, Vitamin K shot given
May breast-feed and hold baby	Physical Apgar test

WHAT'S THE SCORE?

Almost immediately after your baby is born, the attending pediatrician or pediatric nurse will screen the baby to determine if she is healthy and breathing properly and what special care, if any, may be needed in the nursery. The test most commonly used is the Apgar, taken one minute after birth and again five minutes after birth. It rates your baby's physical adjustment to independent living on a scale from zero to ten points. A one-minute rating below *five* may not mean much; a five-minute Apgar score below *five* is possibly significant. There's no need for concern if your baby's score is off one or two points. That's fairly common.

Here's how the Apgar table looks:

	0	1	2
Heart rate	Absent	Under 100 per minute	Over 100 per minute
Respiratory effort	Absent	Slow, gasping	Good, strong cry
Muscle tone	Flaccid	Poor	Active motion
Reflexes	No response	Grimace, some response	Active, crying
Color	Body pale or blue	Body pink, extremities blue	Completely pink

way to get to know your new baby. You will get used to holding her, diapering her, feeding her with a bottle of water. If your wife is nursing, she will have more opportunities to feed the baby.

SIBLING VISITS

Some hospitals allow an older child to visit the hospital. It is often helpful for him or her to see the new baby (through the nursery window) and understand that Mom is okay. If your facility does not allow such visits, make sure your wife calls home every day. In the latter case, you may be obliged to stay at home more so that you can be with your older child.

CIRCUMCISION

If you have a boy baby, you and your wife will have to decide if you want him circumcised, a procedure which removes the foreskin that covers the tip of the penis. As there is no evidence that the foreskin, if left intact, is a potential breeding ground for infection, the decision is a personal one for parents, and will be influenced by cultural or religious concerns rather than by hygiene.

JAUNDICE

If, a couple of days after your baby is born, her skin takes on a color reminiscent of a Florida tan, she has a common condition called jaundice. It is due to an inability of her liver to handle excess red blood cells, which are broken down into a substance called bilirubin. The condition usually disappears within a week.

The hospital will monitor the "bili count" by checking your baby's blood with a heel-prick blood test or a hand-held jaundice meter that measures light reflected from the baby's skin. If the bili count becomes too high (although the policy varies from hospital to hospital, 6 to 7 milligrams/ 100 milliliters serum found in blood is considered safe, 10 to 12 is usually acceptable, and over 15 is unsafe), they will probably put her under special lights for a day or two.

Becoming a Family

BONDING

When you hold your baby, you see a real live human being, wide-eyed and quiet, looking back at you. The contact between you is real. Hold on to these precious moments, because this time can be the entrance into a whole new dimension of your life as a man.

Now that the baby is bundled and nestled in your arms, you will be aware of a tremendous sense of fulfillment. This is only the first step in your growth as a nurturer and provider for this tiny, helpless being. The fathering "instinct," like the maternal "instinct," must be learned. To be successfully integrated into fathering, you must discover who your baby is. You must "bond" with her.

The word is misleading, though. Bonding suggests an action that happens once and is immediately accomplished, as in carpentry or welding; it has mechanical overtones. As we all know, you build human relationships over time; they don't just happen automatically. We suggest that you think, instead, of "attachment," which better expresses the evolution of the connection between father and child.

The key here is physical closeness. There are lots of ways to accomplish this. Hold her every chance you get. Once you are home, carry her in a cloth carrier on your chest on a walk or while you do errands. You will feel her warmth and movements. Body to body, you will begin to communicate: You will feel her dependence; she will feel your protection. As you log time with your baby, you will notice that your feeling for her intensifies.

The bonding process will accelerate if you expand your duties to include taking care of her day-to-day needs. Share the nurturing load (though, naturally, you must work within certain biological and personal limitations).

COMING HOME

The early euphoria of fatherhood will get a boost when you bring your wife and baby home. You've looked forward with such eagerness to this moment. Coming home alone to a dark, blank house after visiting hours are over hasn't been much fun.

If you drove your wife *to* the hospital in a controlled hysteria, you may find that you drive her and the baby home *from* the hospital as if you were carrying a load of eggs. (Remember to install the car safety seat before you go to pick them up. Some hospitals won't release the baby unless you have one.) When you arrive home with your precious cargo, you will be happy that the three of you are finally together under your own roof, not in a hospital room, where you were always a visitor.

Once they have left the professional baby support system provided by the hospital, fathers and mothers alike can feel apprehension and doubt their ability and resources to do the job. A newborn baby's sleep and eating patterns are disorganized; she cries a lot. Parents are not sure what the baby needs, or when she needs it. It will be two to six weeks before their baby settles down to a predictable schedule.

CRYING TIMES

It is important to remember, as you and your wife work through these early weeks, that your baby has no more idea of what's going on than you do. You won't always be able to fix the problem. In the early going, parenting is based on the not-so-scientific method of trial and error. A baby cries for reasons other than hunger and fatigue, and she won't be able to sit up and tell you. You will develop a repertoire of techniques for these cranky times which will often soothe the baby and help her to stop crying.

DEVELOPING A MENTAL CHECKLIST

The only way your baby can tell you something is wrong is by crying. You will learn to respond to her cue by running down a list of possible causes. You will start with the most likely one and move down the list until an answer is found—or at least she has stopped crying.

- Is she hungry?
- Is she tired?
- Is she bored?
- Is she overstimulated?
- Is she ill (feverish, drawing up her legs in pain or showing other signs of discomfort)?
- Is she upset because the people around her are upset? (Babies pick up on the moods of others from a very early age.)
- Is she feeling lonely and needs some cuddling? (Don't worry that picking her up will "spoil" her—you can't spoil a young baby.)

Babies often cry during the cocktail/dinner hour. For no apparent reason your baby is inconsolable. You can be a big help. You can take over dinner while your wife nurses and calms her. Alternatively, you may find yourself at the helm of the baby carriage, making consecutive circles around the block. Going for a ride in the car can work wonders, too.

Other solutions for other crying times: You may find that placing her on her tummy over your knees and gently patting or rubbing her back will help to bring up a gas bubble. Or she may be crying because she is bored being in one position. Try turning her from her back to her tummy, or vice versa.

Experiment with motion. She will usually quieten when you pick her up, put her over your shoulder and walk around. A ride in a cloth carrier on Daddy's chest will often soothe the unhappiest baby.

THIS IS NOT A CONTEST

Go with whatever works, but be ready to improvise when you discover that what works one day won't work the next. *Don't* take it personally if she doesn't stop. *Don't* see it as success or failure. Too often new parents equate their ability to soothe their baby with their ability to nurture their baby. *Don't* put your ego on the line.

This is not a contest with your partner to see who can dry tears faster. Of course, you want the baby to be comfortable and happy. All parents want the best for their baby. The problem is—now and later—that it can't always be. Babies are hardy creatures. They survived the rather harrowing birth experience. They can survive inexperienced parenting with ease. Your baby will thrive both because of you and in spite of you.

Differences Unite

Daddies deal with their babies quite differently from mommies. They handle them in a much more physical way. Mommies are gentle and careful, and worry over details of the baby's comfort. You greet her, play with her, hold and carry her in ways that are all your own. Don't let the differences you see bother you. They are both natural and desirable.

Your baby probably wouldn't have it any other way. If it were possible to have two people acting in exactly the same

THE FOOTBALL HOLD

Many a father enjoys carrying his baby around like a football. This leaves one arm free for other duties. You can try it, too:

Sunny side up. In the first weeks after birth, when the baby can't hold her head up at all, lie her on her back, cradling her head in your hand. Align her body along your arm. Her legs will naturally fold up into the fetal position. Rest your arm on your body for added support of her body.

The flip side. As she learns to hold her head off the mattress when lying on her tummy, she will have sufficient strength to hold her head up while she lies on her tummy along your arm. Hold her shoulders and upper chest in your hand and allow her legs to straddle the crook of your elbow. As with the earlier hold, rest your arm on your body to help support her body.

way, how boring it would be! You can be sure that she is taking everything in; infants are knowledge sponges. She will respond to each of you differently. She is learning that there's value in differences. Can you imagine anything more important for her than discovering that there's spontaneity in life, surprise and love that aren't defined by an off-the-shelf formula?

A word or two of caution, however. In the early weeks after birth, a newborn must assimilate a lot of new sensations. Leaving the dark security of the womb, she enters our bright, airy world jammed with stimulation. She discovers hunger, texture and space for the first time. Overstimulation can prolong her period of adjustment. Later, as she learns to sit, crawl and walk, she is rapidly expanding the world she knows by leaps and bounds. She may find spontaneity too much to handle at the end of the day or when she is ready for a nap. Don't overdo a good thing.

Feeding Your Baby

The decision between bottle- and breast-feeding is very personal and it is best if you participate in the selection. You and your wife will have to weigh many important variables in making the choice. Your baby's nutrition, your wife's career or job, and your attitudes and expectations are some factors to consider. Get the facts about both methods. Examine your feelings and weigh the pros and cons.

BREAST-FEEDING

If your wife nurses your baby, you will not be able to feed the baby on a regular basis. The only bottles she will get will be occasional relief bottles. But there is satisfaction in the knowledge that your baby is getting nature's perfect food along with some important immunities against certain diseases. You can find alternate ways to care for your baby. If she enjoys a bath, you can take over that routine as a way to soothe her and be close to her.

As your wife and baby settle into breast-feeding, they become a nursing couple. Their closeness may seem to shut you out. This feeling of alienation can hurt and fester unless you talk it over with your wife. Communicating your feelings will help defuse the problem.

BOTTLE-FEEDING

If your baby is bottle-fed, you can share the joy (and exhaus-

---

ANOTHER BOTTLE POSITION

The traditional method of feeding a baby a bottle is to hold her head nestled in the crook of your arm, with her body lying along your arm.

Here's an alternative that promotes eye contact and helps her learn your face and its expressions while she drinks:

Sitting down with your legs together and your feet propped on a low stool, lie the baby along the niche created by your legs. Her head should be elevated by your knees, her legs curled up naturally into your lap.

---

tion) of feeding times. You can derive real pleasure in giving her the nourishment she wants and needs. You may choose the early morning and the just-before-bedtime bottles as your special time with her. Be sure to help with the daily bottle cleaning and formula preparation as often as possible. It's only fair that you share the chores as well as the fun.

A Personal Challenge

The father's dual role of nurturer/provider is a challenging one. Be prepared to discover some difficulties in reconciling the two. You will almost certainly be caught up in it the moment you start thinking about providing for your new family. There's a tender new life in your charge, someone completely dependent on you for food, clothing and shelter, not to mention the truckload of money needed for a college education.

BATHTIME STRATEGIES

It's probably not nearly as difficult as you think it is to give your baby a bath:

Newborns should have a sponge bath *without soap.* All you need is a soft washcloth, a small container of warm (but not hot) water, some cotton balls, a mild baby shampoo, a contoured baby bath sponge for her to lie in, a soft towel, cream if needed, a fresh diaper and a change of clothes. Make sure the room is warm enough and that you have everything before you start. Handle her firmly, but gently. *Never* leave her unattended, even for a moment.

1. Gently undress the baby except for her diaper in the same place where you are going to bathe her. Lie her on the sponge.

2. Rinse the cloth in water and wring it out. Rinse again as needed to keep the cloth warm.

3. Gently wipe her arms, legs and body with the cloth, stopping to dry her as you go. To wash her back, raise her off the sponge, supporting her head with one hand, and wipe with the other.

4. Next, remove the diaper. Clean up any mess with tissues. Then with your wet washcloth wipe the genital and anal areas, paying special attention to the folds and creases. Wipe her bottom from front to back. Gently dry her, smooth on cream and put on a fresh diaper.

5. Wet and squeeze out the cotton balls and wipe her face and ears. Don't poke into her nose. If you spy some dry mucus, you can roll an end of a damp cotton ball into a small point and dab gently up to loosen and remove it.

6. Take special care around her eyes, which are vulnerable to infection in the early days. Tear cotton balls into small pieces. Wet and squeeze out the excess. Wipe once with each piece, going in only one direction, from the nose outward.

7. The final step is the shampoo. With the baby lying on her back, hold her head in your hand, resting her body on your forearm. (Her bottom and legs should rest on the bathing surface.) Hold her head over the pan. Dip the washcloth in the water, squeeze most of it out and use the cloth to dampen her hair. Repeat until her hair is thoroughly wet. Squeeze a drop or two of baby shampoo on your fingers (this is a one-handed trick you can practice), or you can pre-measure a little into the bottle cap. Gently massage her scalp and hair. Rinse as before. Gently towel dry.

An older baby can be bathed lying on her bath sponge in a sink or tub with two inches of water, using the same list of accessories. Be sure the room is warm and use soap sparingly, if at all. Encourage her to kick and play in the water. You can dip your washcloth in the water and squeeze it on her belly. She'll be amazed at the sensation!

Once again, never leave your baby during bath time!

You would be in a tiny minority if you didn't feel that you must work harder, to earn more, to "get ahead," so that you can build a better future for your new family. If your wife stays home, you lose her income. If she returns to work, you will still have a tremendous responsibility to shoulder (and expensive babysitting fees to pay).

Taking the long view, you'll want to plan for your family's future. Make sure that the steps you take are rooted in common sense. For example, take out a life insurance that you can afford and open a savings plan—however small—to get you started. You can increase the amounts of both later on.

Being a good provider is a noble ambition. It also poses a profound dilemma if you want to be a hands-on father, rather than an absentee. How to do both is problematical: Working hard takes you away from your baby. You may not want to observe your baby from beyond the barricade of your job. Though your job may take you away from your baby during the day, you can use the time when you are home to nurture—and play with—her.

Though in some cases men have stayed home while their partners returned to work, most men don't opt to be house-husbands. In a two-career household it is more likely that either your wife will stay home for a while or you will both return to work. If both of you are going back to work, you will then need to enlist the help of a competent caregiver to raise your baby while you are away.

Fathering is a plus equation. Think of all it can add to your life—wider and deeper emotional range; satisfaction

NURTURING BY OTHERS

If your wife plans to go back to work after your baby comes, you will need to decide on the kind of care she should have. Quality of care, affordability and convenience are the most important points to consider in making your choice. As you look into the resources in your area, you will probably find these options:

IN-HOME CARE

Hiring someone to come to your home to care for your baby is expensive but convenient. Your baby has a one-on-one relationship with her caregiver, remains in the environment she is accustomed to, and is less likely to catch colds and other illnesses from other children.

The best sources of candidates for the job are domestic employment agencies, word of mouth, and advertising in the newspaper. Prescreen each applicant over the phone and then interview the best candidates in person. Make sure your baby is there to meet each one. Note carefully how they handle her and how she reacts to them. If you are in doubt, keep looking.

OUT-OF-HOME CARE

There are two basic kinds of out-of-home care: day-care centers and family-care homes. A day-care center cares for a number of children in an institutional atmosphere. Family care is a less formal arrangement in which a woman, often with young children of her own, cares for a few others in return for a reasonable daily or weekly fee.

In a good family-care home your baby will receive quality care and learn how to cope with other children. A good day-care center can be as expensive as in-home care. But it may be worth the expense because it offers a wide range of stimulating activities, professional staff and, of course, other children to play with.

The best sources of out-of-home care are local child-care referral services and word of mouth. If you are exploring options in your area, examine each for health, cleanliness and quality of care. Interview each extensively before making a choice and afterward constantly monitor your baby's situation.

and pride at proving you can do it; new accomplishments, sensitivities, responsiveness, generosity; an expanded sense of meaning, significance and purpose.

As you share the joy and the work of raising a family, you'll hold your baby, rock her, play with her; give her as much of your time, and yourself, as you can. Lying on your chest, she will have the best naps of her life. You and she will get to know each other, and you will belong to each other.

CHAPTER 5

Keeping Your Relationship on Track

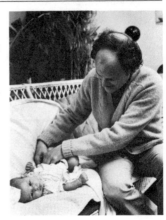

Heads You Win, Tails She Loses

Childbirth affects you and your wife in different and often opposite ways. During pregnancy your wife has been the center of attention. With any sort of luck, everyone has been solicitous of her health and mental state, and mindful of the ordeal yet to come. Now that she has completed her initial assignment, the focus—yours and everyone else's—switches to the baby. In her mind's eye the baby's mother loses her special status. A couple of days after childbirth, she will fall into what's commonly known as postpartum blues.

Not only does she lose her position in the spotlight, she

may have a stomach that hasn't snapped back to its original shape, and the irritating pain of stitches (if she has had a cesarean birth, her discomfort is on a much higher level— she's recovering from abdominal surgery).

Your experience, on the other hand, is the reverse. You're on the receiving end. All at once, your baby, whom you could not approach or know before, is given to you. You'll need to appreciate that your gain is your wife's loss and that she may compensate for this by doting possessively on her infant, particularly if she breast-feeds him.

Avoid joining in a tug-of-war with her. The baby must not be a prize to fight over. If you do, everybody loses, including the baby. If anything will save the day, it is communication. Talk over your feelings. Give your wife the attention and affection she needs.

Opening your heart and sharing feelings with her will help you both to move past the conflict of mother/baby vs. father/baby. Give and take will help the three of you come together.

Sharing the Load

There is a myth floating about that being home with a baby, in and of itself, is a wonderful experience. But babies require repeated, extensive attention that can become tiresome. Parents on the front line need to escape from their demanding little charges. If they don't get away, what start out as acts of loving care can turn into joyless exercises—or worse. The pleasure of tending baby can become soured by the arid vista of never-ending diapering, feeding, bathing, soothing . . . . Burnout is a distinct possibility.

If your wife perceives that she is shouldering the nurturing burden alone, she is likely to be resentful. After all, *you* get to go out into the real world and talk to *real* people. *She's* stuck at home up to her elbows in formula and baby wash. Though by working you take on the all-important provider role—without you, she and the baby would be, quite literally, cold, homeless and hungry—your wife will still begrudge you all the "fun" you find in the outside world.

It is important to work side by side with your wife. If she is at home with the baby during the day, you should be prepared to take on baby duty as soon as you come home. She will welcome relief, particularly if you arrive at the witching hours of early evening. You are fresh (even though tired from work), ready for baby battle; she is weary, ready for reinforcements.

Think of it as tag-team parenting. When one of you is fed up with the baby (and as he grows older, and the "terrible two's" set in, you will know just what that means), you hand off the baby like a baton. The parent gets a break to recoup and return again.

Sharing the care of your baby will boost your adult relationship as well.

Talking together, you can share your feelings about the baby. If you chip in and help out, you will be better equipped to understand *her* feelings. Additionally, your help with the baby reinforces the unity of your tiny family. When you bathe, feed and diaper him, you'll be saying to your wife that you're in this together, and that you take nothing for granted.

This is powerful medicine for calming the emotional stress you're both going through, and will add new, rich dimensions to your relationship.

Jealousy

It will also lay the groundwork for dealing with an emotion that may take you by surprise because it seems so unreasonable, even obnoxious, under the circumstances. That emotion is jealousy.

Here's how it commonly happens. You observe how completely self-enclosed and seemingly natural together your wife and baby are. They're like one person. You look enviously on this closeness and wonder if you can ever attain such an intimacy with your child. You feel you're at a disadvantage because you go to work. It seems unfair.

More disturbing is the way the baby can take over your wife. You're losing the private space with her that once was exclusively yours; he has appropriated it. Intimate moments, quiet times, when you and your partner could shut out the world, are up for grabs, and baby takes all. Despite your deepest longings you often feel you're an outsider, and you don't want to be outside either wife or baby. The hateful word "rejection" crowds out more positive emotions and thoughts.

Of course the baby makes a difference in your relationship with your wife. With a third person added to your life, particularly a helpless, dependent one, you can't expect business as usual. Hard as that may be to accept, it's perfectly natural.

The first step is to explore your feelings with your wife. Ignored or buried, they'll fester and poison the relationship. She'll understand negative feelings. She has them too. You have been companions and lovers. No more than you does she want to lose something that is as invaluable to her as it is to you.

Grandparents Are Free

What's needed at this moment is for the two of you to change the details of your relationship so that they match the change your baby has introduced. The solution isn't difficult, but it does take joint, planned effort.

Call it time-out from parenting, *your* time, *quality* time. You need the opportunity to recover the sense that you and your wife are people with needs and emotions of your own as well as responsible parents of a little baby.

Reserve one or two days a week when you two can plan to go out for dinner and a movie or stay in for a sexual evening. What you crave now are relaxing, private interludes. A couple of hours two times a week will do wonders for your morale and your relationship.

Find sitters who can be retained on a regular basis. Pay them extra to keep them loyal. Grandparents (are free), referrals from a domestic service, an ad in the paper or yellow pages, or a neighborly widow are all sources of babysitting services. With the exception of grandparents, in-depth interviews filled with "what if" questions are strongly recommended.

To simplify the time it takes to plan your nights out, it may work to schedule Wednesday and Saturday evenings. With a phone call or two, you can make arrangements for your evenings out a month at a time. Don't worry about the cost. Remember: Babysitters are cheaper than psychiatrists!

This means time away from your baby, a prospect that may make you and your wife uncomfortable. This infant, both before birth and since, has absorbed massive amounts of your attention and energies, and without realizing it you've built a wall around your existence with him. You're not sure you can move outside it. But you *have* to. You and your wife risk emotional suffocation if you don't let fresh air into the cloistered environment of parenting.

Sexual Relations

During the six-week postpartum period, when you and your partner abstain from sex, she becomes daily more desirable to you. While you are waiting out this period, there are sexually gratifying alternatives to full lovemaking that you can adopt, and she can experience orgasm without running any risk of physical harm.

Once this period is behind you and you're back on the lovemaking track, you probably won't be surprised that it runs along a much different route from before. The reason, of course, is the presence of your baby. His demands for attention are likely to interrupt your lovemaking or may leave you both so exhausted that sleep is preferable to sex.

Unfortunately, there's another problem that can sabotage conjugal bliss. Don't be disappointed or disillusioned if sexual desire revives in her at a slower pace than you would like. It takes time for the radical physical changes that occurred in her during pregnancy to shift back to normal. In addition to nature, real-life adjustment to mothering takes its toll as well. Up with the baby during the night and going nonstop all day, she's tired. And if she's nursing, hormonal activity makes her even more tired.

Luckily, this period won't last. As the baby sleeps through the night with regularity (it varies from baby to baby, the average is at about six months), you and she will be more rested.

Taking Over

We have said that daily duties that you get into the habit of doing are important. But what about your days off? Think about taking over the baby duty so that your wife can have part or all of a day to herself. (If she is nursing, she will obviously still have to do that piece of the work.) You will get to know your baby and she will have the break she needs.

This plan may not be simple to implement if your wife feels proprietary about the baby. To her, caring for him means more than executing a clutch of physical tasks; it enables her to fulfill her image of the mother role. These day-to-day activities can be a mirror in which your wife may read, and measure, her maternal performance. Lots of profound emotions may be at work here.

Taking over will be easier if you discuss your intentions before the baby comes and start doing baby duty from Day One. If you learn your way around the nursery together,

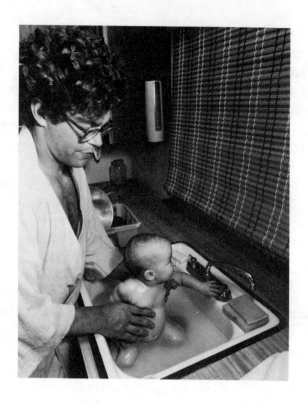

and do it with a sense of humor, then you start off even. If she stays home with the baby and you go back to work after the baby is born, she will necessarily learn more about baby care. You will have to cram into off-work hours what she has all day to do.

Talking over your role as a nurturing father before the baby is born sets the stage for give-and-take later on. If she agrees beforehand that she is going to share the baby's care with you, there will be fewer emotional firestorms once the star of the show has arrived. As the baby settles in at home, you can adapt your baby **chores** to fit your schedule and your wife's needs.

As we have said before, **don't compete** for *"Best Parent."*

Reprise

As you read this guide to becoming a father, it may seem that we've set out an endless obstacle course for you to run. It has been nothing but do this here, give more there, don't complain, be patient, it will all be worth it in the end. You leap one hurdle and there's another one ahead of you, and the promised land seems as insubstantial as smoke.

The trouble with language, a great writer once said, is that it's only words. Well, unfortunately, language is all we have to tell you about the tremendous benefits of exploring the role of father, of growing into it. A film you see, or the sight of friends in action with their babies, may contribute immediacy, but they're still only words made visible.

The bottom-line truth is that you can't be a father ahead of time any more than you can be in love before it happens. Chances are you'll be a better father, and lover, by having some advance understanding of what to expect from each experience, of where the pitfalls are and how to avoid them—or extricate yourself if you happen to stumble into one.

But when it comes to the extraordinary difference that nurturing and loving a baby can make in your life, there's no alchemy that can turn plain words into gold. You can't know the difference until you try it.

Doing is believing.

Believe.

Bibliography

SPECIFICALLY FOR FATHERS

Daddy: The Diary of an Expectant Father, by Dennis Denziger (Tucson, AZ: HP Books, 1987).

Father and Child: Developmental and Clinical Perspectives, by S. Cath, A. Gurwitt and J. Ross (Boston: Little, Brown, 1982).

Fathering, by Maureen Green (New York: McGraw-Hill, 1976).

How to Father, by Fitzhugh Dodson (New York: New American Library, 1974).

Fathering, by C. Phillips and J. Anzalone (St. Louis: C.V. Mosby, 1978).

How to Be a Pregnant Father, by Peter Mayle (Secaucus, NJ: Lyle Stewart, 1977).

New Father Survival Guide, by Larry Snydal and Carl Jones (New York: Franklin Watts, 1987).

The Expectant Father, by George Schaefer (New York: Barnes and Noble, 1972).

The Father: His Role in Child Development, by D. Lynn (Monterey, CA: Brooks-Cole, 1974).

The Father's Almanac, by S. Adams Sullivan (Garden City, NY: Doubleday, 1988).

The Liberated Man, by Warren Farrell (New York: Random House, 1975).

The Role of the Father in Child Development, by M. Lamb (New York: John Wiley, 1976).

GENERAL

The Maternity Sourcebook: 230 Basic Decisions for Pregnancy, Birth and Baby Care, by Matthew and Wendy Lesko (New York: Warner Books, 1984).

PREPARING FOR PARENTHOOD

Planning Ahead for Pregnancy: Dr. Cherry's Guide to Health, Fitness and Fertility, by Sheldon H. Cherry M.D. (New York: Viking, 1987).

Letters to a Child Never Born, by Oriana Fallaci (New York: Doubleday, 1976).

A Baby? . . . Maybe, by Elizabeth M. Whelan, Sc.D. (New York: Bobbs-Merrill, 1976).

LIFE IN THE WOMB

A Child Is Born, by Lennart Nilsson (New York: Dell, 1976).

The First Nine Months of Life, by Geraldine Lux Flanagan (New York: Simon & Schuster, 1962).

The Secret Life of the Unborn Child, by Thomas Verny (New York: Summit, 1981).

HAVING BABIES LATER IN LIFE

Having a Baby After 30, by Elisabeth Bing and Libby Colman (New York: Bantam, 1975).

Parents After Thirty, by Murray Kappelman and Paul Ackerman (New York: Wideview Books, 1981).

The Pregnancy After 30 Workbook, by Gail Brewer (Emmaus, PA: Rodale Press, 1978).

Pregnancy After 35, by Carole McCauley (New York: Pocket Books, 1976).

NUTRITION IN PREGNANCY

Eating Right: Before, During and After Pregnancy, by Elisabeth Whelan (New York: American Baby Books, 1982).

Nourishing Your Unborn Child: Nutrition and Natural Foods in Pregnancy, by Phyllis Williams (New York: Avon, 1975).

ADULT NEEDS IN PREGNANCY AND PARENTING

Making Love During Pregnancy, by Elisabeth Bing and Libby Colman (New York: Bantam, 1977).

The Private Life of Parents: How to Take Care of Yourself and Your Partner While Raising Happy, Healthy Children—A Complete Survival Guide, by Roberta Plutzik and Maria Laghi (New York: Everest House, 1983).

Sex, by Michael Carrera (New York: Crown Publishers, 1981).

BIRTH PLAN ALTERNATIVES

Birth Without Violence, by Frederick Leboyer (New York: Knopf, 1980).

The Complete Book of Midwifery, by Barbara Brennan and Joan Rattner Heilman (New York: E.P. Dutton, 1979).

The Rights of the Pregnant Patient: How to Have an Easier, Healthier Hospital Birth Together, by Valmai Howe Elkins (New York: Two Continents Publishing Group, 1976).

Shared Childbirth: A Guide to Family Birth Centers, by Philip Sumner and Celeste Phillips (St. Louis: C. V. Mosby, 1982)

CHILDBIRTH METHODS

Awake and Aware: Participating in Childbirth Through Psycho-prophylaxis, by Irwin Chabon (New York: Delacorte, 1974).

Childbirth Without Fear, by Dr. Grantly Dick-Read (New York: Harper & Row, 1959).

The Complete Book of Pregnancy and Childbirth, by Sheila Kitzinger (New York: Knopf, 1980).

A Husband-Coached Childbirth, by Dr. Robert Bradley (New York: Harper & Row, 1974).

Methods of Childbirth, by Constance Bean (New York: Dolphin Books, 1982).

Prepared Childbirth, by Tarvez Tucker (New Canaan, CT: Tobey Publishing Company, 1975).

Six Practical Lessons for an Easier Childbirth, by Elisabeth Bing (New York: Bantam, 1969).

Thank You, Dr. Lamaze, by Marjorie Karmel (New York: Dolphin Books, 1965).

CESAREAN BIRTH

Cesarean Childbirth, by Christine Coleman Wilson and Wendy Roe (New York: Signet, 1980).

Cesarean Birth Experience, by Bonnie Donovan (Boston: Beacon, 1977).

Silent Knife, by Nancy Wainer Cohen and Lois Estner (South Hadley, MA: J.F. Bergen Publishers, 1983).

PREMATURE BIRTH

Born Early, by Dr. Mary Ellen Avery and Georgia Litwack (Boston: Little Brown, 1983).

Premature Babies: A Handbook for Parents, by Sherri Nance (New York: Arbor House, 1982).

ADJUSTING TO BABY

New Parenthood: The First Six Weeks, by Cecilia Worth with Anna Marie Brooks (New York: McGraw Hill, 1985).

Index